EULENBURG AUDIO+SCORE

Georges Bizet

Carmen
Suite No. 1

Based on the critical edition / Nach der kritischen Ausgabe von
Robert Didion

EULENBURG

EAS 176
ISBN 978-3-7957-6576-7
ISMN 979-0-2002-2587-7

Ernst Eulenburg Ltd
48 Great Marlborough Street
London W1F 7BB

Contents / Inhalt

Preface

Composed: 1875; the first suite was arranged after Bizet's death; different arrangements/versions exist
Instrumentation: 2 Flutes, 2 Oboes, 2 Clarinets, 2 Bassoons – 4 Horns, 2 Trumpets, 3 Trombones – Timpani, Triangle, Tambourine, 2 Drums, Cymbal – 2 Harps – Strings
Duration: ca. 14 minutes

When Georges Bizet died on 3 June 1875 just months short of turning 37, it was exactly three months previously to the day that his final opera *Carmen* had been given its world premiere. The evening of the first performance was anything but a success for the composer; following an initially favourable reaction, the atmosphere progressively cooled and the evening culminated in a fiasco. As later reported by one of Bizet's colleagues, the co-librettist Ludovic Halévy, 'the fourth act was received in an icy atmosphere':[1] Bizet was heart-stricken.

On the evening of the first performance, no-one could have imagined that the composition would ultimately become one of the most frequently performed works in the entire operatic repertoire. Only a year later, its triumphal procession throughout the world began, albeit far away from Paris: Brussels and Budapest were followed by Stockholm, Dublin, New York, London, Melbourne, Hamburg, Prague, Milan, Mexico City, Buenos Aires, Malta, Riga, Lisbon and Amsterdam – and these were only a few of the first destinations of the opera. Tchaikovsky's response (as a member of the audience in St Petersburg during the performance of *Carmen* in 1878) appeared to have been proved true: 'I am certain that *Carmen* will be the most popular opera in the whole world in ten years' time.'[2] In view of this incredibly swift success story, the debacle in Paris appears all the more incomprehensible, and it is worth pursuing the reasons for such a negative reaction.

Several years prior to his concrete plans for *Carmen*, Bizet had urged for 'more realism' and it was he who suggested the plot for his next opera project, the novella by Prosper Mérimée, published in 1845, based on a true story: the bandit Don José falls for the wild libidinal urges on the part of the gypsy Carmen and finally kills her because she does not reciprocate his love. The libretto by Henri Meilhac and Ludovic Halévy tones the story down somewhat in comparison to Mérimée's novella: many aspects are less brutal and cold (for example, Don

---

[1] Ludovic Halévy, 'La millième représentation de Carmen', in: *Le Théâtre* (Paris, 1905), 5–14
[2] Quoted from: Attila Csampai/Dietmar Holland (Ed.), *Georges Bizet, Carmen. Texte, Materialien, Kommentare* (Reinbek, 1984), 298

José mutates from a wild and hot-tempered murderer to a wavering lover), but enough was retained to deeply confound both the audience and professional critics: the work was set in a contemporary period in a dubious milieu, with a cast of female workers, soldiers and gypsies. At the heart of the opera was an unscrupulous and amoral woman who abandons herself to her lust for life – and this in blatant opposition to the respectable society ladies of the 1870s. This was carried to its extremes by the occurrence of the final tragedy, the murder on stage, which takes place on the outer fringes of society. Up until this time, music theatre had adhered to the rules of lofty stylistic tradition in which the tragic figure was confined to the upper regions of society and the comic figures predominantly undertaken by more 'common' persons. (Giuseppe Verdi had of course acted as a pioneer for Bizet with his opera *La traviata* which focused on the life and death of a Parisian courtesan, but this had 'only' been an Italian opera). In *Carmen*, the different social spheres were however thoroughly blended with one another – so directly that the singer originally envisaged for the title role relinquished her part for the reason that the frivolous role of Carmen and her tragic end did not appear to correspond with each other.

The press took exception to both the plot and the music to equal degrees, declared the role of Carmen to be 'thoroughly disagreeable', accused the work of being 'immoral' and Bizet (of all people!) as a follower of Wagner – the criticism could not have been more adverse for a composer in the (cultural-)politically heated period after 1871. However, nothing could hit the mark as precisely as the overall verdict: 'Quelle vérité, mais quel scandale!' ('What realism, but what a scandal!'[3])

Bizet once described himself and his abilities to his best friend, the composer Ernest Guiraud, as follows: 'Your place is in (grand) opera. For myself, I fear that I lack the necessary depth. I will shine in comic opera: I will extend and transform this art-form.'[4] Bizet was to be proved right as far as the opera *Carmen* was concerned which was a milestone in the history of the genre. The composer had however greatly overrated his public who were not in the least inclined to approve of the path he had taken, that is until the international success of the opera paved the way for its return journey back to Paris.

Prominent amongst Bizet's stage works preceding *Carmen* is his incidental music to Daudet's play *L'Arlesiénne* (1872). Although the play itself barely lasted for a run of three weeks, the quality of Bizet's contribution was well received by the critics and it was at the direct suggestion of Johannès Weber of *Le Temps* that Bizet selected and rescored some of the numbers for concert performance. The premiere of this reworked material as the first *L'Arlesienne* suite took place on 10 November 1872 at the *Concerts Populaires*. The orchestral material was subsequently published by Choudens, Paris, and has retained its popularity in the orchestral repertoire ever since.

[3] Edgar Istel, 'Die Uraufführung, die Pariser Presse, die Galli-Marié und der Tod Bizets', in: Csampai/Holland, *Carmen*, 190, 193
[4] ibid., 186f

It was appropriate, then, that Choudens, who were responsible for the publication of *Carmen*, should again publish two suites of orchestral numbers derived from that opera. In this case, there was however an initial problem with the authenticity of the material. Following the first performance of the opera in March 1875, there had been plans to stage the work in Vienna in the autumn of the same year, but with recitatives in place of the spoken dialogue of the original version. Bizet's sudden death in June 1875 initially thwarted these plans; Choudens subsequently entrusted Bizet's friend Ernest Guiraud with this task. Guiraud, unfortunately, did not merely limit himself to the composition of the recitatives; he also added three dance movements and abridged other passages, cut out an entire number, revised the instrumentation and created innumerable variations which would enable the title role to be sung by a soprano. It was Guiraud's non-authentic version which formed the basis for the printed edition of all parts including the score, and this arranged version was how the world became initially acquainted with Bizet's opera.

It was only in the last few years that this fundamental philological desideratum was produced; with the aid of an abundance of existing source material in Paris, Robert Didion created a reconstruction of Bizet's originally intended version which has been published as a study score. The editor presents a meticulous but simultaneously fascinating description of the great confusion surrounding Bizet's original version of his *Carmen*.[5]

The two suites have also been produced on the basis of this new edition; the order of movements adheres to the version published by Fritz Hoffmann in the Dover edition (New York). In contrast to Bizet's own four-movement adaptation of his first *L'Arlésienne-Suite* with an almost symphonic structure, Fritz Hoffmann's version of the Carmen suites both contain six movements. This also stands in contrast with Chouden's earlier five movement edition of both suites. The original keys of the operatic version have been retained.

There is no attempt in the two suites to relate the unhappy love story between Don José and the libidinal Carmen in chronological order. Musical-dramatic aspects have been the decisive factor for the order of movements which repeatedly spring back and forth between the four acts of the opera. What is noticeable is that the first suite is made up exclusively of instrumental pieces from the opera with the exception of one movement (No. 4), whereas the movements of the second suite all originated as vocal numbers (choruses, ensembles and solo movements).

The first suite is framed by the overture of the opera which is split into its two very different halves; the tempestuous beginning which sets the opera in action and the grand march for the entrance of the toreadors in the arena in the final act are reserved for the final movement of the suite (No. 6). Instead, the suite opens with the second section of the opera overture which evokes a dark and mysterious atmosphere with its famous 'Fate' motif; in the operatic version, this section also foreshadows the impending tragedy and leads into the first scene

---

[5] Robert Didion, in the preface to the score of *Carmen*. Study score Eulenburg (Schott) No. 8062 (Mainz, 1992), IX–XII.

(No. 1, Prelude). The slow initial movement is followed by the *Aragonaise*, an *Allegro vivo* (No. 2) which in the opera forms the final entr'acte following Act III and sets the scene with its tempestuous 3/8 *Allegro vivo* for the beginning of the fourth act in which the market traders offer their wares in the square in Seville. The movement No. 3 of the Suite (Intermezzo) is identical to the entr'acte music before Act III which leads into the smugglers' chorus in the mountains. The Intermezzo is the lyrical point of rest, not only from the aspect of tempo (Andantino, quasi Allegretto), but also due to its intimate chamber musical instrumentation, particularly at the beginning: the flute solo is played over tranquil arpeggios on the harp. With Carmen's *Séguedille* (No. 4), the lascivious fervour of the title figure is brought into play, and at this point, the arrangement has to alter the instrumentation of the original version; the missing vocal part is initially undertaken by the oboe which is later coupled with other instruments (trumpet and then clarinet). Flute, oboe, two clarinets and bassoon even join forces to produce a more intensive tonal effect in Carmen's final verse. The movement No. 5 (*Les dragons d'Alcala*) utilises the last remaining entr'acte music of the opera forming the transition between Acts I and II in which Carmen is shown together with her comrades who then dance together. The brief movement (Allegro moderato) is characterised by a strikingly original instrumentation; the melody is played by the two bassoons above pizzicato strings accentuated by the tambourine – an evocation of the dark world of the gypsies. In contrast, the final movement No. 6 (*Les toréadors*) with its extrovert music for large orchestra marking the entrance of the toreadors returns to the material of the overture.

Ursula Kramer
Translation: Lindsay Chalmers-Gerbracht

Vorwort

komponiert: 1875; die Suite wurde erst nach dem Tod Bizets zusammengestellt; es existieren unterschiedliche Arrangements
Orchesterbesetzung: 2 Flöten, 2 Oboen, 2 Klarinetten, 2 Fagotte – 4 Hörner, 2 Trompeten, 3 Posaunen – Pauken, Triangel, Tamburin, 2 Trommeln, Becken – 2 Harfen – Streicher
Spieldauer: etwa 14 Minuten

Als Georges Bizet am 3. Juni 1875 noch nicht einmal 37-jährig starb, lag die Uraufführung seiner letzten Oper *Carmen* auf den Tag genau drei Monate zurück. Es war ein düsterer Abend für den Komponisten gewesen. Nach anfänglicher Freundlichkeit kühlte die Stimmung mehr und mehr ab, und am Ende stand ein Fiasko: Wie Bizets Mitstreiter, einer der beiden Librettisten, Ludovic Halévy, später berichtete, war „der vierte Akt mit eisiger Kälte aufgenommen"[1] worden. Bizet war zutiefst getroffen.

Dass das Werk sich schließlich zu der bis heute am meisten gespielten Oper des Repertoires überhaupt mauserte, mochte wohl am Abend der Uraufführung niemand ahnen. Dabei begann der Siegeszug durch die Welt schon ein Jahr später, allerdings fernab von Paris: Auf Brüssel und Budapest folgten Stockholm, Dublin, New York, London, Melbourne, Hamburg, Prag, Mailand, Mexiko City, Buenos Aires, Malta, Riga, Lissabon, Amsterdam – um nur ein paar der ersten Stationen der Oper zu nennen. Tschaikowskys Einschätzung (er hatte *Carmen* 1878 in St. Petersburg als Zuschauer erlebt) schien sich zu bewahrheiten: „Ich bin überzeugt, dass in zehn Jahren Carmen die populärste Oper der ganzen Welt sein wird."[2] Umso unverständlicher scheint nach dieser raschen internationalen Erfolgsgeschichte das Debakel von Paris, und es lohnt, nach den Gründen dafür zu fragen.

Schon einige Jahre vor den konkreten Plänen zu *Carmen* hatte Bizet „mehr Realismus" angemahnt, und er selbst schlug schließlich den Stoff für sein neues Opernprojekt vor, die 1845 erschienene Novelle von Prosper Mérimée, die auf einer wahren Begebenheit beruhte: Der Bandit Don José verfällt der wilden Triebhaftigkeit der Zigeunerin Carmen und bringt sie schließlich um, weil sie seine Liebe nicht erwidert.

---

[1] Ludovic Halévy, „La millième représentation de Carmen", in: *Le Théâtre*, Paris 1905, S. 5–14.
[2] Zitiert nach: Attila Csampai/Dietmar Holland (Hg.), *Georges Bizet, Carmen. Texte, Materialien, Kommentare*, Reinbek 1984, Zeittafel S. 298.

Zwar wurde im Libretto von Henri Meilhac und Ludovic Halévy gegenüber der Novelle von Mérimée manches abgemildert, erschien nun weniger hart und kalt (so ist Don José vom wilden, hitzigen Mörder zum zaudernden Liebhaber mutiert), doch blieb wahrlich noch genug übrig, was das Publikum mitsamt den professionellen Kritikern zutiefst irritierte: Das Stück spielte in der Gegenwart, in einem fragwürdigen Milieu; Arbeiterinnen, Soldaten und Zigeuner bevölkerten die Szenerie. Im Zentrum eine skrupellose, amoralische Frau, die sich ihrer Lebensgier hingibt und damit das krasse Gegenstück zu den wohlanständigen Damen der Gesellschaft der 1870er Jahre darstellte. Auf die Spitze wurde das Ganze dadurch getrieben, dass sich in dieser Randzone der Gesellschaft mit dem Mord auf offener Szene eine finale Tragödie ereignete. Bis dahin hatte man im Musiktheater an der alten Stilhöhenregel festgehalten, nach der das Trauerspiel Figuren hohen Standes vorbehalten war, während das heitere Genre vorzugsweise von „gewöhnlichem" Personal bedient wurde. (Giuseppe Verdi war Bizet freilich als Pionier vorausgegangen, indem auch er das Leben und den Tod einer Pariser Kurtisane ins Zentrum seiner Oper *La traviata* gerückt hatte, aber es war schließlich „nur" eine italienische Oper gewesen.) Nun aber wurden die Sphären jäh miteinander vermischt – und das so unvermittelt, dass sogar die ursprünglich für die Titelrolle vorgesehene Sängerin ihre Partie wieder zurückgab, mit der Begründung, der leichtfertige Charakter der Carmen und das tragische Ende schienen nicht zusammenzupassen.

Die Presse nahm am Stoff wie an der Musik gleichermaßen Anstoß, fand die Rolle der Carmen „schrecklich unangenehm", warf dem Werk „Immoralität" vor und bezichtigte Bizet (ausgerechnet!) der Gefolgschaft Wagners. Schlimmer hätte die Kritik in der (kultur)-politisch aufgeheizten Zeit nach 1871 für einen Komponisten kaum ausfallen können. Doch nichts traf den Kern der Sache besser als das Gesamturteil: „Quelle vérité, mais quel scandale!" („Welche Realistik aber was für ein Skandal!"[3])

Gegenüber seinem besten Freund, dem Komponisten Ernest Guiraud, hatte Bizet sich und seine Fähigkeiten einst folgendermaßen eingeschätzt: „Dein Platz ist in der (großen) Oper. Was mich betrifft, so fürchte ich, dass mir die Weite dafür fehlt. In der komischen Oper werde ich glänzen: ich werde die Kunstart erweitern, sie umformen."[4] Was die Sache selbst anging, sollte Bizet für seine *Carmen* unbedingt recht behalten: Sie war ein Meilenstein in der Geschichte der Gattung. Sein Publikum hatte der Komponist hingegen reichlich überschätzt: Es mochte den von ihm eingeschlagenen Weg zunächst nicht gutheißen, und erst der internationale Erfolg ebnete der Oper den Weg zurück nach Paris.

Unter Bizets Bühnenwerken aus der Zeit vor *Carmen* ragt insbesondere seine Bühnenmusik zu Daudets Schauspiel *L'Arlésienne* (1872) heraus. Obwohl das Stück selbst kaum drei Wochen lief, kam Bizets Beitrag bei den Kritikern gut an, und auf Vorschlag von Johannès Weber von *Le Temps* wählte Bizet einige der Nummern aus und bearbeitete sie für Konzertaufführungen. Die Uraufführung dieses überarbeiteten Materials als erste *L'Arlésienne-*

---

[3] Edgar Istel, „Die Uraufführung, die Pariser Presse, die Galli-Marié und der Tod Bizets", in: Csampai/Holland, *Carmen*, a. a. O., S. 190, 193.

[4] Ebda., S. 186f.

Suite fand am 10. November 1872 bei den *Concerts Populaires* statt. Das Orchestermaterial wurde später vom Pariser Verlag Choudens herausgegeben und hat seitdem seine Popularität innerhalb des Orchesterrepertoires bewahrt.

Entsprechend sollte der Verlag Choudens, der für die Veröffentlichung von *Carmen* verantwortlich war, damals noch zwei Suiten mit Orchesternummern aus dieser Oper herausgeben. Doch gab es hier von Anfang an ein Problem mit der Echtheit des Materials. Nach der Uraufführung der Oper im März 1875 sollte das Werk im Herbst des gleichen Jahres in Wien in Szene gehen, allerdings mit Rezitativen anstelle des gesprochenen Dialoges in der Originalfassung. Bizets plötzlicher Tod im Juni 1875 durchkreuzte diese Pläne zunächst, doch Choudens beauftragte schließlich Bizets Freund Ernest Guiraud mit dieser Aufgabe. Dieser beließ es allerdings nicht bei den Rezitativ-Ergänzungen; auch drei Tanzeinlagen kamen hinzu, dafür kürzte er an anderen Stellen, strich eine Nummer komplett, retuschierte die Instrumentation und erfand zahllose Varianten, um die Partie der Titelrolle auch für Sopranistinnen zugänglich zu machen. Es war diese nicht-authentische Version Guirauds, die den gedruckten Einzelausgaben inklusive der Partitur zugrunde gelegt wurde, und nur in dieser bearbeiteten Form lernte die Welt Bizets Oper kennen.

Erst in den letzten Jahren wurde dieses grundlegende philologische Desiderat aufgearbeitet. Robert Didion rekonstruierte anhand der umfänglich erhaltenen Quellen in Paris die von Bizet selbst intendierte Fassung, die als Studienpartitur erschienen ist. In seinem Vorwort erläutert der Herausgeber so akribisch wie spannend die Gemengelage um Bizets Originalversion seiner *Carmen*.[5]

Auf der Basis dieser neuen Edition werden nun auch die beiden Suiten vorgelegt; sie folgen im Ablauf ihrer Sätze der von Fritz Hoffmann im Verlag Dover (New York) herausgebrachten Ausgabe. Im Unterschied zu der von Bizet selbst vorgenommenen Adaption seiner ersten *L'Arlésienne*-Suite, der er mit der Viersätzigkeit eine regelrecht symphonische Disposition verlieh, umfasst die Version der *Carmen*-Suiten von Fritz Hoffmann zweimal sechs Sätze. Damit unterscheiden sich diese auch von der einst bei Choudens erschienenen, jeweils nur fünf Nummern umfassenden Edition der beiden Suiten. Die originalen Tonarten der Oper werden beibehalten.

Weder in der ersten noch in der zweiten Suite wird versucht, die Geschichte der unglücklichen Liebe von Don José zur triebhaften Carmen chronologisch nachzuerzählen. Vielmehr spielen musikalisch-dramaturgische Gesichtspunkte die entscheidende Rolle für die Aufeinanderfolge der einzelnen Nummern, und es wird immer wieder zwischen den vier Akten hin- und hergesprungen. Auffällig ist jedoch, dass die erste Suite mit Ausnahme einer Nummer (Nr. 4) sämtlich aus reinen Instrumentalsätzen der Oper (Ouvertüre und Zwischenaktmusiken) besteht, während es sich bei allen Sätzen der zweiten Suite im Original um vokale Nummern handelte (Chöre, Ensembles und Solonummern).

---

[5] Robert Didion, Vorwort zur Partitur Carmen. Studienpartitur Eulenburg (Schott) Nr. 8062. Mainz 1992, S. IX–XII.

Den Rahmen der ersten Suite bildet das Vorspiel der Oper, das dafür in seine beiden im Charakter sehr unterschiedlichen Teile aufgespalten wird: Der stürmische Beginn, mit dem die Oper anhebt, und der Einmarsch der Toréadors in die Arena im letzten Akt werden nun für den Schluss (Nr. 6) reserviert. Stattdessen beschwört die Eröffnungsnummer der Suite gleichsam unvermittelt die düster-unheimliche Atmosphäre mit dem berühmten Schicksalsmotiv herauf, das in der Opernversion erst den zweiten Teil der Ouvertüre bildet und dort – gleichsam als „Ahnung" der bevorstehenden Tragödie – in die erste Szene hineinführt (Nr. 1, Prélude). Der langsamen ersten Nummer folgt mit der *Aragonaise* ein *Allegro vivo* (Nr. 2); es handelt sich um die letzte Zwischenaktmusik der Oper im Anschluss an den III. Akt. Sie stimmt im stürmischen 3/8 *Allegro vivo* auf den Beginn des IV. Aktes ein, als die Händler auf dem Platz in Sevilla ihre Waren feilbieten. Nr. 3 der Suite (Intermezzo) ist identisch mit der Zwischenaktmusik vor dem III. Akt, der mit dem Chor der Schmuggler im Gebirge anhebt. Es ist der lyrische Ruhepunkt, der sich nicht nur durch ein entsprechendes Tempo (*Andantino, quasi Allegretto*), sondern auch durch eine geradezu intim-kammermusikalische Instrumentierung, besonders am Anfang, auszeichnet: Über ruhigen Harfenarpeggien spielt die Flöte ihr Solo. Mit Carmens *Séguedille* (Nr. 4) kommt die laszive Glut der Titelfigur ins Spiel, und hier muss das Instrumentalarrangement nun erstmals in die Originalpartitur eingreifen: Die fehlende Singstimme wird anfangs durch die Oboe, später in Kopplung mit anderen Instrumenten (Trompete, dann Klarinette) ersetzt. Um klanglich intensiverer Schlusswirkung willen wird Carmens letzte vokale Strophe schließlich gar von Flöte, Oboe, zwei Klarinetten und Fagott gemeinsam gespielt. Mit Nr. 5 (*Les dragons d'Alcala*) liegt das letzte Zwischenaktstück vor: der Übergang vom I. zum II. Akt, der Carmen mit ihren Gefährten zeigt und sie zusammen tanzen lässt. Die kurze Nummer (*Allegro moderato*) zeichnet sich durch eine ganz eigene instrumentale Klangfärbung aus: Über gezupften Akkorden der Streicher, unterstützt vom Tamburin, liegt die Melodie in den beiden Fagottstimmen – gleichsam dunkel die Welt der Zigeuner beschreibend, während sich mit der Nr. 6 (*Les toréadors*) und der fulminanten Auftrittsmusik der Toréadors mit großem Orchester der Bogen zum Vorspiel schließt.

Ursula Kramer

Carmen
Suite No. 1

Georges Bizet
(1838–1875)

I. Prélude

Andante moderato (♩ = 58)

EAS 176

Edited by Richard Clarke
© 2011 Ernst Eulenburg Ltd, London
and Ernst Eulenburg & Co GmbH, Mainz

2

4

II. Aragonaise

6

12

III. Intermezzo

IV. Séguedille

26

V. Les dragons d'Alcala

VI. Les toréadors

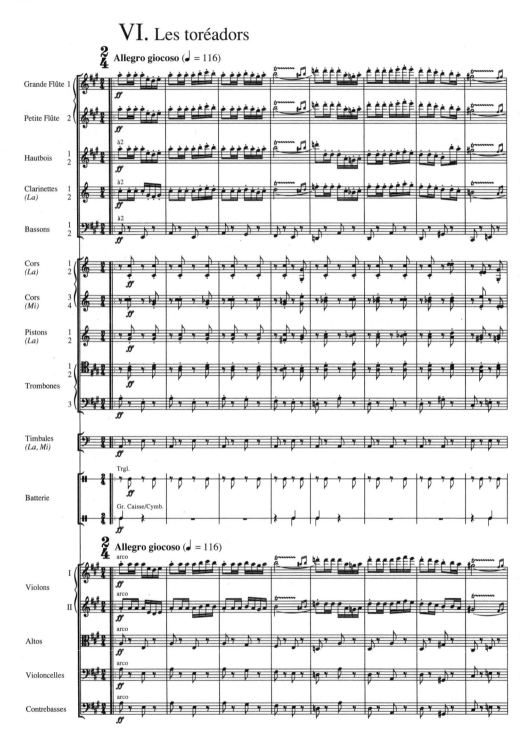

44

F

EAS 176

Printed in China

THE ART OF SCORE-READING

The first steps

A score contains the entire musical text of a musical work in order that the conductor and everyone who wants to study the piece more thoroughly can see exactly which passages are being played by the orchestra or ensemble. The parts of the individual instruments are arranged in such a way that all notes played at the same time are written one below the other.

Scores help us to listen to, understand and interpret musical works. Those who only listen to music are unaware of many important details which, after some practice, become apparent when reading the score while listening to the music. The clear structure of the score helps to easily understand the compositional style and the characteristic features of a piece – this is a prerequisite not only for any analysis but also for the musician's own performance and interpretation.

The simplest method of score-reading is to read an individual part by concentrating on an individual part that can be heard particularly well. The most suitable pieces to begin with are concertos with solo instruments such as Beethoven's Romance in F major for violin and orchestra (example 1) or orchestral songs (with them, one may easily follow the text). Furthermore, in many classical orchestral works, it is quite easy to follow the lead part of the principal violin, or the bass part in baroque compositions for orchestra.

The next step is to try to change from one part to another and vice versa and follow the part that is leading. Little by little, you learn to find distinctive parts you hear in the score as well and follow them in the corresponding staff. This can be very easily tried out with Beethoven's Symphony No. 5 (example 2). To read the score, it is also helpful to count the bars. This technique is rather useful in the case of confusing or complex scores, such as those of contemporary music, and is particularly suitable when you do not want to lag behind in any case. It should be your aim, however, to eventually give up counting the bars and to read the score by first following individual parts and then going over to section-by-section or selective reading (see next page).

Example 1 · from: Romance for violin and orchestra in F major by Beethoven

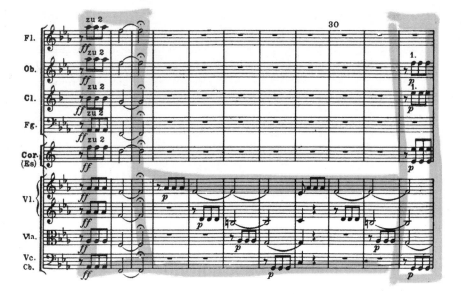

Example 2 · from: Symphony No. 5 C-minor by Beethoven

Further score-reading techniques

Example 3 · from: Symphony No. 100 G major 'Military' by Haydn

Example 4 · from: Symphony No. 41 C major 'Jupiter' by W. A. Mozart

Section-by-section reading

This technique is suitable for application in the 'Military' Symphony by Haydn (example 3). In bb. 260-264, the parts are mostly in parallel motion so that it is quite easy to take in the section as a whole. In the strings, the texture is homophonic (i.e. all instruments play the same rhythm), consisting of tone repetitions in the lower parts while there is a little more movement in the part of the first violin. At the same time, the tones of the winds are stationary (i.e. long sustained notes), serving as harmonic filling-in. If need be, they can also be read en bloc.

Such block-like structures often consist of unison figures (= all instruments play the same), such as at the beginning of Mozart's Jupiter Symphony (example 4). Here, the score-reading can first be limited to the strings section which carries the melody alone in bb. 3-4 and contains all important information.

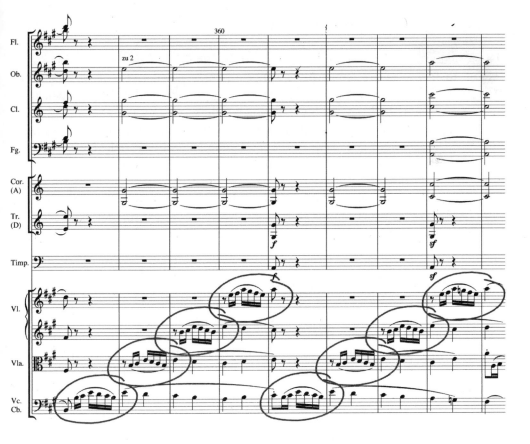

Example 5 · from: Symphony No. 7 A major by Beethoven

Selective reading

Using this technique, you concentrate on selected parts (lead parts, conspicuous passages) in the score. In the excerpt from Beethoven's Symphony No. 7 (example 5), it is the semiquaver motif that, originating with the violoncellos and basses and pervading the string parts twice, is particularly well suited. The stationary tones of the winds, consisting only of the note E in various octave positions in bb. 358-363, form the harmonic foundation and play a subordinate role in score-reading. Though they are briefly noticed, it is the strings and especially the conspicuous semiquaver motif pervading the individual parts that are to be followed.

With both score-reading techniques which should be chosen according to the nature of the passage in question, it is not important in the beginning to be able to follow at once all tones and harmonies. What matters more is to recognize and comprehend sequences of movement. Everything else comes with experience.

Following contrapuntal parts

The present excerpt from Brahms's Requiem (example 6) is polyphonic, i.e. one has to be able to follow several equal parts either alternately (without lagging behind) or simultaneously. But by looking for parallel parts in the score, the notation which, at first glance, seems to be overcrowded soon becomes clearer. For example, Brahms allocates orchestral parts to each choral part. As a consequence, there are many parts written in the score but considerably fewer independent parts actually played. Hence, the large amount of written music can be reduced to a manageable quantity.

The flute, clarinet, first violins and soprano are in parallel motion. Furthermore, the tenor of oboe and viola is supported by a much-expanded, yet parallel part.
The violoncellos and bassoons too are in almost parallel motion.

The low winds and strings as well as the timpani played simultaneously with the polyphonic parts are fill-in parts which consist only of stationary tones (sustained notes). They do not need to be followed upon first reading of the score.

Seen as a whole, this excerpt is most suitable for focussing on the soprano voice as it is coupled with two instruments and, being the highest voice, can be heard very well. In addition, the text is an aid to orientation, making it easier to return from brief trips to other parts.

In fugal sections, score-reading will be easier if the entries of the theme in the score are first looked for and then marked.

Example 6 · from: A German Requiem by Brahms

The score at a glance

A **Bar lines** are solid vertical lines within the instrument sections.

B The **bar numbers** are an aid to orientation in the score. Sometimes capital letters, so-called rehearsal letters, are used instead of numbers.

C The system of parallel lines on and between which the notes are written is called **staff** (or stave). The instrument abbreviation in front of each line (here, Fl. is for 'flute') indicates to which instrument(s) the line(s) refer(s).

D The **barline at the left-hand end** of the staves connects all staves to form the **system**.

E In addition to the barline at the left-hand end of the staves, **angular brackets** connect the individual groups of instruments in a score (wind, brass and string instruments). Within these groups, the instruments are arranged according to their pitch, with the highest-pitched instrument mentioned first.
Today, the common order of instrumental parts in the score is as follows, from top to bottom:
· wind instruments
· brass instruments
· percussion instruments
· harp, piano, celesta
· solo instrument(s)
· solo voices
· choir
· string instruments

F When there are two systems on a page, they are separated from each other by two parallel **diagonal strokes**.

G Instruments the names of which are followed by 'in Bb' or (Bb) are **transposing instruments**. In this case, (Bb) indicates that the notated C is played as Bb, i.e. all tones are played a tone lower than notated. Most of the transposing instruments are easily recognizable in the score thanks to these additions. However, there are also transposing instruments without such indications in the score, such as:
· piccolo flute (in C / an octave higher)
· cor anglais (in F / a fifth lower)
· contrabassoon (in C / an octave lower)
· double bass (in C / an octave lower)

H The transposing brass instruments have no general signature but, if need be, accidentals preceding the respective tone.

I The viola part is notated in the **alto clef**, the parts of violoncello and bassoon sometimes in the **tenor clef**. Both clefs are easy to read when the player realizes that the clef frames the note C1:
alto clef   tenor clef   treble clef

J Any change of key or time is marked by a **double bar**. The alla-breve sign following in this example (¢), like the sign for four-four time (c), is a relic from an old notational practice and stands for two-two time.

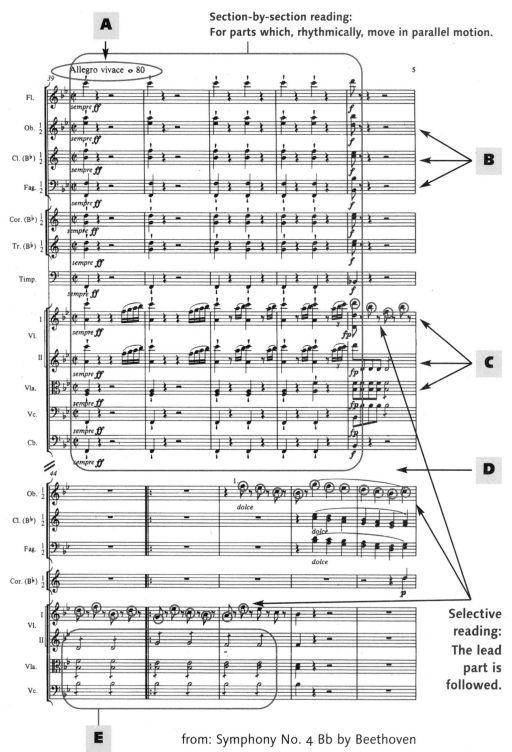

Section-by-section reading:
For parts which, rhythmically, move in parallel motion.

Selective reading: The lead part is followed.

from: Symphony No. 4 Bb by Beethoven

A **Tempo indications** (sometimes in connection with metronome markings) are used by the composer to indicate how fast a piece shall be played.

B In the winds, two parts are usually brought together in one line. If they play the same note, the note head either has two stems or 'a2' written above it.

C Two-part chords in the staves of the strings are played by one player. If the parts shall be divided, **divisi** (divided) is written in the score. Then, at each desk, one player plays the upper notes and another player the lower notes.

D When an instrumental part contains a long rest, as in this flute part for example, its staff is often omitted until the next entry of the instrument, thus saving space. In addition, there are less page-turns, and the playing parts are arranged much clearer.

E In order to save space and arrange phrases or groups of notes more clearly, so-called abbreviations are used occasionally. The sign ♩ stands for ♪♪♪♪, with the minim indicating the duration of the repetitions and the stroke crossing the stem indicating the value of the notes to be repeated (1 stroke = quaver, 2 strokes = semiquaver, etc.). Cf. also the viola in b. 43 in which the repeated notes are first written out and then abbreviated.

Score-Reading with pupils and students!

Order this guideline for score-reading for your class! The leaflet 'The Art of Score-Reading' is available separately or as a set of copies and can be obtained free of charge while stock last.

Brochure 'The Art of Score-Reading'
Order No. ETP 9998-99 (free of charge)

Mozart for the classroom

A picture of life and travel
Mozart was not only one of the greatest composers, but also one of the best pianists of the 18th century. Like the virtous of today, he spent a large part of his life on concert tours at the leading courts and great cities of his time.

This small brochure depicts a panorama of the musical life in Europe wich formed the background to Mozart's oeuvre. The picture is completed by a short biography and a little insight into his way of composing.

Brochure 'Mozart. A Picture of Life and Travel'
Order No. ETP 9991-99 (free of charge)

For further information, see at: www.eulenburg.de

Eulenburg

DIE KUNST
DES PARTITURLESENS

Der erste Einstieg

Eine Partitur enthält den gesamten Notentext eines Musikwerkes, damit der Dirigent und jeder, der sich näher mit dem Stück beschäftigen will, genau nachvollziehen kann, was das Orchester oder das Ensemble spielt. Dabei sind die Instrumente so angeordnet, dass alle Noten, die zur gleichen Zeit erklingen, genau untereinander stehen. Partituren helfen beim Hören, Begreifen und Interpretieren von Musikliteratur. Wer nur zuhört, erkennt viele kostbare Kleinigkeiten nicht, die beim Mitlesen nach ein wenig Übung regelrecht sichtbar werden. Der Kompositionsstil und die Charakteristik eines Werkes lassen sich mit der übersichtlichen Partitur schnell begreifen – das ist nicht nur Grundvoraussetzung für jede Analyse, sondern auch für das eigene Spiel.

Die einfachste Methode beim Partiturlesen ist das Verfolgen einer Einzelstimme. Bei diesem Verfahren konzentriert man sich auf eine einzelne Stimme, die besonders gut zu hören ist. Zum Einstieg eignen sich dabei besonders gut Konzerte mit Soloinstrumenten wie die Romanze in F-Dur für Violine und Orchester von Beethoven (Beispiel 1) oder Orchesterlieder (bei letzteren kann man sich leicht am Text orientieren). Weiterhin kann man bei vielen klassischen Orchesterwerken die führende Stimme der ersten Violine gut verfolgen, sowie bei barocken Kompositionen für Orchester die Bass-Stimme.

In einem nächsten Schritt kann man versuchen, zwischen den Stimmen zu wechseln und jeweils die Stimme zu verfolgen, die gerade führend ist. Nach und nach lernt man dabei markante Stimmen, die man hört, auch in der Partitur zu finden und im entsprechenden Notensystem zu verfolgen. Besonders anschaulich kann man das mittels Beethovens 5. Symphonie erproben (Beispiel 2).
Eine weitere Hilfe beim Lesen der Partitur kann auch das Mitzählen der Takte sein. Dieses Verfahren hilft bei unübersichtlichen oder komplexen Partituren wie etwa zeitgenössischer Musik und eignet sich besonders, wenn man den Anschluss auf keinen Fall verlieren möchte. Ziel sollte es jedoch sein, das Mitzählen der Takte gänzlich zu verlassen und die Partitur zunächst anhand einzelner Stimmen und dann im Wechsel von blockweisem bzw. selektivem Lesen zu verfolgen (siehe nächste Seite).

Beispiel 1 · aus: Romanze für Violine und Orchester F-Dur von Beethoven

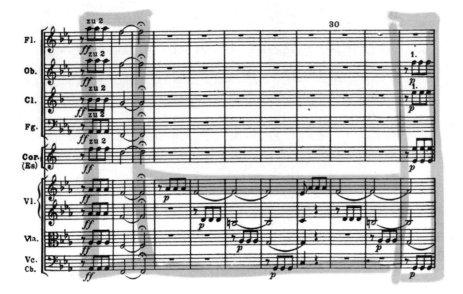

Beispiel 2 · aus: Symphonie Nr. 5 c-moll von Beethoven

Weitere Methoden des Partiturlesens

Beispiel 3 · aus: Symphonie Nr. 100 G-Dur „Militär" von Haydn

Beispiel 4 · aus: Symphonie Nr. 41 C-Dur „Jupiter" von W. A. Mozart

Blockweises Lesen

Diese Methode bietet sich in der Militär-Symphonie von Haydn an (Beispiel 3). In den T. 260-264 sind die Stimmen weitgehend parallel geführt, so dass man sie gut im Ganzen überblicken kann. In den Streichern haben wir einen homophonen Satz (d.h. alle Stimmen spielen den gleichen Rhythmus), der in den unteren Stimmen aus Tonwiederholungen besteht, während die erste Violine etwas bewegter ist. Gleichzeitig erklingen in den Bläserstimmen Liegetöne (d.h. lang ausgehaltene Töne), die als harmonischer Füllstoff dienen. Sie können bei Bedarf auch im Block gelesen werden.

Oft bestehen solche blockhaften Gebilde auch aus unisono-Figuren (= alle Stimmen spielen dasselbe), wie z.B. am Beginn der Jupiter-Symphonie von Mozart (Beispiel 4). Hier kann man sich beim Lesen zunächst nur auf den Streicherblock beschränken, der in den T. 3-4 alleine die Melodie weiterführt und bereits alle wichtigen Informationen enthält.

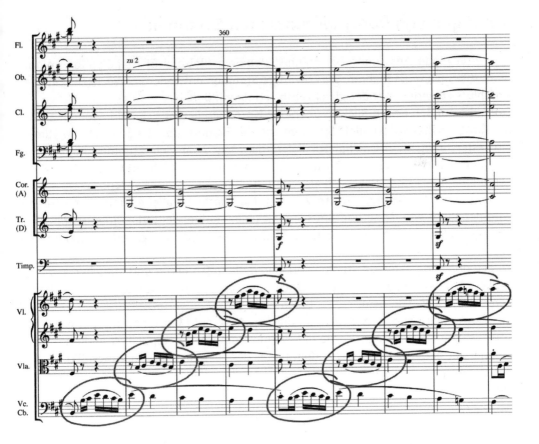

Beispiel 5 · aus: Symphonie Nr. 7 A-Dur von Beethoven

Selektives Lesen

Bei dieser Methode orientiert man sich anhand ausgewählter Stimmen (führende Stimmen, auffällige Stellen) in der Partitur. Im Ausschnitt aus Beethovens 7. Symphonie (Beispiel 5) ist hierzu das Sechzehntelmotiv geeignet, das zweimal von den Celli und Bässen ausgehend durch die Streicherstimmen wandert. Die Liegetöne der Bläser, die in den T. 358-363 sogar nur aus dem Ton e in unterschiedlichen Oktavlagen bestehen, bilden die harmonische Grundierung und spielen beim Lesen der Partitur eine untergeordnete Rolle. Man nimmt sie kurz wahr, verfolgt jedoch die Streicher und dort insbesondere das auffällige Sechzehntelmotiv in seiner Wanderung durch die einzelnen Stimmen.

Bei beiden Leseformen, zwischen denen man übrigens je nach Beschaffenheit der Stelle wechseln sollte, kommt es am Anfang nicht darauf an, sofort alle Töne und Harmonien verfolgen zu können. Viel wichtiger ist es, Bewegungsabläufe zu erkennen und nachzuvollziehen. Alles Weitere kommt mit der Erfahrung.

Verfolgen von kontrapunktischen Stimmen

Der vorliegende Ausschnitt aus Brahms' Requiem (Beispiel 6) ist polyphon komponiert, d.h. man muss mehrere gleichwertige Stimmen entweder im Wechsel (ohne den Anschluss zu verlieren) oder gleichzeitig verfolgen können.

Doch das auf den ersten Blick so übervolle Notenbild lichtet sich bald, wenn man sich die Partitur näher auf parallele Stimmen ansieht. Brahms ordnet z.B. jeder Chorstimme Orchesterstimmen zu. Das hat zur Folge, dass hier zwar viele Stimmen notiert sind, aber wesentlich weniger eigenständige Stimmen tatsächlich erklingen. Die vielen geschriebenen Noten lassen sich also auf ein überschaubares Maß reduzieren.

So werden Flöte, Klarinette, erste Violinen und Sopran parallel geführt. Des Weiteren wird der Tenor von Oboe und Bratsche mit einer stark erweiterten, aber dennoch parallel verlaufenden Stimme unterstützt. Ebenfalls fast ganz parallel verlaufen Violoncelli und Fagotte.

Zu den polyphon gefügten Stimmen erklingen die tiefen Bläser und Streicher sowie die Pauke mit Füllstimmen, welche lediglich aus Liegetönen (ausgehaltene Töne) bestehen. Sie braucht man beim ersten Lesen nicht weiter zu verfolgen.

Im Ganzen gesehen bietet sich in diesem Ausschnitt an, schwerpunktmäßig die Sopranstimme zu verfolgen, da sie mit zwei Instrumenten gekoppelt ist und als höchste Stimme gut herauszuhören ist. Zudem bietet der Text eine Orientierungshilfe, so dass der Wiedereinstieg von vorübergehenden Ausflügen in andere Stimmen erleichtert wird.

Bei fugierten Abschnitten kann man sich das Mitlesen auch erleichtern, indem man zunächst alle Einsätze des Themas in der Partitur sucht und sich markiert.

Beispiel 6 · aus: Ein deutsches Requiem von Brahms

Die Partitur im Überblick

A **Taktstriche** sind innerhalb der Instrumentengruppen durchgezogen.

B Die **Taktzahlen** erleichtern die Orientierung in der Partitur. Manchmal dienen hierzu auch Großbuchstaben, sog. Studierbuchstaben.

C Eine einzelne Zeile der Partitur nennt man **Notensystem**. Für welche(s) Instrument(e) sie steht, zeigt der **Instrumentenvorsatz** an (hier Fl. für Flöte).

D Der **Kopfstrich** verbindet alle Notensysteme miteinander zu einer **Akkolade**.

E Zusätzlich zum Kopfstrich fassen **gerade Klammern** die einzelnen Instrumentengruppen (Holz-, Blech- und Streichinstrumente) zusammen. Innerhalb dieser Gruppen sind die Instrumente nach Tonlage geordnet, wobei das höchste an oberster Stelle steht.
Die heute übliche Partituranordnung lautet von oben nach unten:
· Holzblasinstrumente
· Blechblasinstrumente
· Schlaginstrumente
· Harfe, Klavier, Celesta
· Soloinstrument(e)
· Solostimmen
· Chor
· Streichinstrumente

F Stehen zwei Akkoladen auf einer Seite, werden sie durch zwei **Schrägstriche** voneinander abgetrennt.

G Steht hinter dem Instrumentennamen z.B. „in B" oder (B), handelt es sich um ein **transponierendes Instrument**. In diesem Fall deutet das (B) an, dass das notierte C als B erklingt, also alle Noten einen Ton tiefer erklingen als sie notiert sind. Die meisten transponierenden Instrumente sind in der Partitur durch diese Zusätze leicht zu erkennen. Es gibt aber auch transponierende Instrumente ohne eine entsprechende Angabe in der Partitur, wie z.B.:
Piccoloflöte (in c/eine Oktave höher)
Englischhorn (in f/eine Quinte tiefer)
Kontrafagott (in c/eine Oktave tiefer)
Kontrabass (in c/eine Oktave tiefer)

H Die transponierenden Blechblasinstrumente haben keine Generalvorzeichen, sondern bei Bedarf Versetzungszeichen, die direkt vor der jeweiligen Note stehen.

I Die Viola oder Bratsche wird im **Altbzw. Bratschenschlüssel** notiert, die Stimmen des Violoncellos und Fagotts manchmal im **Tenorschlüssel**. Beide Schlüssel sind leicht zu lesen, wenn man sich klarmacht, dass der Schlüssel den Ton c1 umrahmt, also:

Alt-   Tenor-   Violinschlüssel

J Vor einem Wechsel der Ton- oder Taktart steht immer ein **Doppelstrich**. Das hier folgende Alla-Breve-Zeichen (¢) ist ebenso wie das Zeichen für den 4/4-Takt (c) ein Relikt aus einer älteren Notationspraxis und steht für den 2/2-Takt.

68

Blockweises Lesen:
Bei rhythmisch parallelgeführten Stimmen.

Selektives Lesen:
Man verfolgt die führende Stimme.

aus: Symphonie Nr. 4 B-Dur von Beethoven

A Durch die **Tempoangabe** (manchmal mit einer Metronomzahl verbunden) gibt der Komponist an, wie schnell ein Stück gespielt werden soll.

B Bei den Bläsern werden in der Regel zwei Stimmen in einer Notenzeile zusammengefasst. Spielen sie den gleichen Ton, erhält der Notenkopf zwei Hälse oder es steht a2 darüber.

C Zweistimmige Akkorde in den Notensystemen der Streicher werden von einem Spieler gespielt. Will man die Stimmen aufteilen, schreibt man **divisi** (geteilt). Dann spielt an jedem Pult ein Spieler die oberen und ein Spieler die unteren Noten.

D Hat eine Stimme, wie hier die Flöte, längere Zeit Pause, wird ihr Notensystem oft bis zum erneuten Einsatz der Stimme weggelassen. So wird Platz gespart, man muß weniger blättern und die erklingenden Stimmen sind übersichtlicher angeordnet.

E Um Platz zu sparen und Tonfolgen übersichtlicher zu gestalten, verwendet man gelegentlich sogenannte **Abbreviaturen (Faulenzer)**. Das hier verwendete Zeichen ♩ steht für ♪♪♪♪, wobei die Halbe Note die Dauer der Wiederholungen anzeigt und der Strich durch den Notenhals den Wert der zu wiederholenden Noten (1 Strich = Achtel, 2 = Sechzehntel usw.). Vgl. auch die Viola in T. 43, in der zunächst die Repetitionen ausgeschrieben und dann abgekürzt sind.

Partiturlesen im Klassensatz

Diese kurze Einführung können Sie als kostenloses Faltblatt bestellen – gern auch im Klassensatz!

Faltblatt "Die Kunst des Partiturlesens"
Bestellnummer: ETP 9999-99 (kostenlos)

Die passende Ergänzung für Klassen- und Unterrichtsräume:

Plakat A2 "Die Partitur im Überblick"
Bestellnummer ETP 9950-99 (kostenlos)

Mozart im Klassensatz

Ein Lebens- und Reisebild
Mozart war nicht nur einer der größten Komponisten, sondern auch einer der besten Pianisten des 18. Jahrhunderts. Wie heutige Virtuosen verbrachte er große Teile seines Lebens auf Konzertreisen zwischen den führenden Höfen und großen Städten seiner Zeit. Diese kleine Broschüre entfaltet ein Panorama des europäischen Musiklebens, das den Hintergrund für Mozarts Schaffen bildete. Eine Kurzbiographie und ein kleiner Einblick in seine Schreibweise runden das Bild ab.

Faltblatt "Mozart. Ein Lebens- und Reisebild"
Bestellnummer ETP 9990-99 (kostenlos)

Weitere Informationen unter www.eulenburg.de

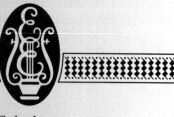

Eulenburg